Ailbhe McDonagh

it's a piano thing

BOOK 2

BOOSEY&HAWKES

AILBHE McDONAGH

Ailbhe McDonagh is an Irish composer and international cellist based in Dublin, Ireland. She is a member of the cello faculty of the Royal Irish Academy of Music, Dublin.

Ailbhe began composing at an early age and won first prizes for composition at 'Feis Ceoil', (the Irish National Music Festival) and at the Royal Irish Academy of Music. While still at school in 2002, the first of her pieces was published when the RIAM Local Centre Examinations (Irish National Grade Examination System) included *Anastasia* in their Grade 4 examination syllabus collection.

Ailbhe studied composition, cello and piano at university in Ireland. She continued her studies in composition at the Eastman School of Music in Rochester, New York, USA while studying for her Masters Degree in Performance on cello.

Ailbhe composes for all instruments and ensembles. She has been commissioned to write pieces from international festivals to school ensembles.   As a cellist, she performs worldwide as a soloist and chamber musician, and released her debut album – *It's A Cello Thing* – in 2012. Most well-known for her compositions for piano for children, Ailbhe has had numerous compositions published by the RIAM Examinations System resulting in her pieces being performed nationally by thousands of children in Ireland.

For further information visit **www.ailbhemcdonagh.com**

Published by Boosey & Hawkes Music Publishers Ltd
Aldwych House
71–91 Aldwych
London
WC2B 4HN

www.boosey.com

© Copyright 2017 by Boosey & Hawkes Music Publishers Ltd

ISMN 979-0-060-13364-0
ISBN 978-1-78454-312-9

First impression 2017

Printed by Halstan:
Halstan UK, 2-10 Plantation Road, Amersham, Bucks, HP6 6HJ. United Kingdom
Halstan DE, Weißliliengasse 4, 55116 Mainz. Germany

Cover design by Chloë Alexander Design (chloealexanderdesign.dphoto.com)

Ailbhe McDonagh

it's a piano thing

BOOK 2

PERFORMANCE DEMONSTRATION TRACKS ⓪1

The enclosed CD contains demonstation tracks for all pieces in this book, performed by the composer.

Visit **www.boosey.com/pianothing** to access digital audio files.

NIGHT CAT ①

AILBHE McDONAGH

This piece has a jazzy vibe and should feel relaxed. Your hands must have a starting position close to the black keys because of their frequency in the key signature. The left hand is mostly *legato* while the right hand playfully alternates between *staccato* and *legato*. Enjoy all the sycnopation – as well as the more unusual experience of crossing the right hand over the left hand for the final low note.

SECRET GARDEN ②

AILBHE McDONAGH

This piece imagines the magic of discovering a secret garden. Soaring melodies are the goal here. The first phrase is 16 bars long. It has a sentence-like structure, with two smaller sub phrases preceeding a longer one. Thinking of long phrases in this way helps to feel and shape the flow of the music more effectively. When the left hand has the accompaniment feature, keep beats 2 and 3 light.

RAZZLE DAZZLE ③

AILBHE McDONAGH

Swing all the quavers in this piece. The first triplet should be smooth even though the fingering is tricky. Pay attention to the *staccato* quaver in the third bar. Once you have mastered the rhythm and articulation for the first two bars in the right hand, the rest of the piece should be relatively straightforward. Watch out for bar 15 – it's easy to forget to swing the two quavers in the left hand.

CLOUDSCAPES ④

AILBHE McDONAGH

Picture the view of a blanket of clouds as seen from an aeroplane window. The left hand accompaniment in this piece should be balanced in favour of the lower voice, with the upper of the two voices sounding more softly. Let the melody in the right hand soar out over the left hand until the left hand takes over the tune itself. The quavers at the final section should be very *legato* and not interrupted by any unintended accents.

GAGAKU 05

AILBHE McDONAGH

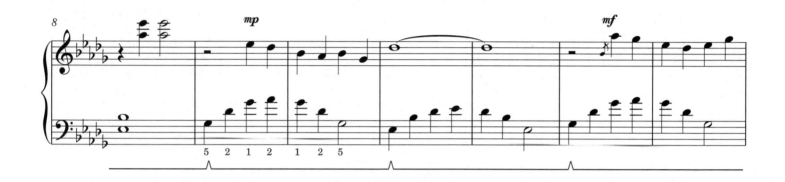

This is a piece written entirely on the black notes of the piano, making the music 'pentatonic' – formed of a five note scale. 'Gagaku' literally means 'elegant music' and is a traditional form of classical music from Japan, written using the same scale as the one used here. It is very important to create an atmosphere in this piece. Be gentle, and always aim for a very smooth *legato*.

BLUE AND GREEN ⑥

AILBHE McDONAGH

The opening of this piece starts in a lower register of the piano than most pieces in this collection. Be careful with the amount of pedal used at the beginning to avoid making the sound muddy and unclear. In bar 13, the right hand melody should sing out over a softer left hand. If possible, bring out the lower notes in the left hand and lighten the higher off-beats while maintaining the *legato* feel. Keep the right hand in a strong hand position for the final chord so that all four notes sound together.

This piece is intended to be played with a straight rhythm – but you could always try playing it swung too...

MARIMBA DANCE ⑦

AILBHE McDONAGH

Coordination is the biggest challenge in this piece. Keep all the *staccato* notes short and light throughout. Be prepared for the places where the pattern changes. The two-note chords in the right hand should be evenly balanced and played exactly together. Enjoy the different feel of 2 or 3 in each bar where it arises – for example, the opening 16 bars should have the feel of a $\frac{6}{8}$ bar followed by a $\frac{3}{4}$ bar on repeat.

ANASTASIA ⑧

AILBHE McDONAGH

Aim for a beautiful singing *legato* sound in the right hand; think of the long phrases and try not to allow any interuption. The lower voice is the more important of the two in the left hand, so to create the correct balance in sound ensure that the inner voice is always softer than the right hand and the lower voice.

WINTER ROSE ⑨

AILBHE McDONAGH

The melody in this piece should sound easy, pure and *legato*. It must soar out above the left hand even though the left hand is often playing something more intricate. At the opening, make sure that the left hand E is always softer than the notes on the beat. Use of the pedal here can be very effective. The left hand has a difficult role throughout with tricky fingering in places: try to practise these spots so that there are no bumps in the sound – as if there is no change at all.

RAT RACE ⑩

AILBHE McDONAGH

Have fun with your chromatic fingering! There is a great contrast between the *legato* of the right hand and the playful *staccato* of the left hand. Try to keep the left hand off-beats lighter than beats 1 and 2. In bar 19, the right hand must use a rocking motion from right to left to help shape this motif effectively.

STEPHEN'S GREEN ⑪

AILBHE McDONAGH

The interesting challenges in this piece are the rhythmic ties in the right hand: to have a relaxed smooth jazzy sound while playing these correctly is the ultimate goal. Look out for the moments where the left hand pattern moves position. Practise the join between these so that they sound seamless. When you have two-note chords in the right hand, sing out the top line. The grace notes before the last chord should be fast and before the beat.

CAROUSEL ⑫

AILBHE McDONAGH

All semiquavers here are *legato* while all quavers are *staccato*. Pay attention to the accent on the 2nd quaver whenever it happens. Sometimes the phrase in the right hand ends but the left hand continues on. The demisemiquavers appear very suddenly so look ahead to be prepared for their arrival.

SUPER SLALOM ⑬

AILBHE McDONAGH

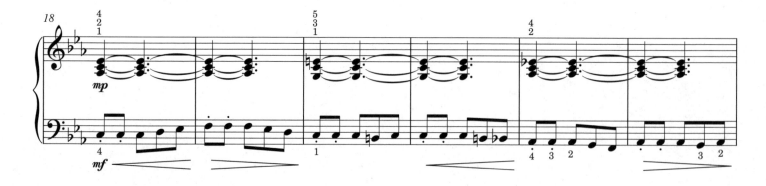

The most challenging aspect of this piece is the $\frac{5}{8}$ rhythm – particularly where you do not have consistent quaver notes. Look at the articulation in the majority of the piece: two notes played *staccato* followed by three *legato* notes. Be sure to make this difference clear. When the tune shifts to the left hand, make the right hand softer so that the tune can be heard. Overall, this piece should have a light feel and the repeated notes should never become heavy or harsh.

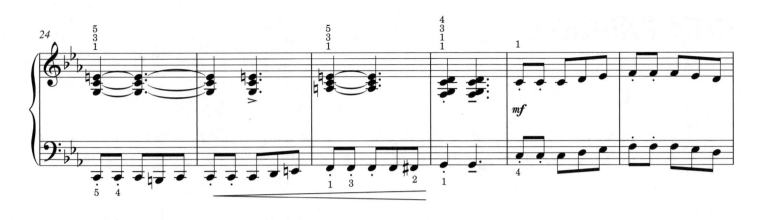

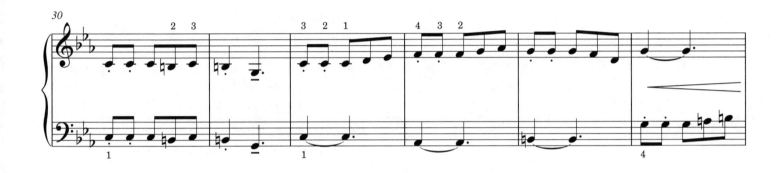

CITY EXPRESS ⑭

AILBHE McDONAGH

For the entire opening of this piece, the left hand has the tune; you must make sure that it sings out more than the right hand. Keep the right hand short (apart from the tiny slurs) and play the thirds exactly together so that they are evocative of the motion of a train. The left hand solo opens the middle section at bar 11. Pay close attention to the articulation here. Watch out for the various right hand rhythms and the tricky three-against-four rhythmic juxtaposition in bar 17. There are some challenging moments in this piece, especially where both hands are playing material with different articulation.

ALSO AVAILABLE FROM BOOSEY & HAWKES